POCKET PUZZLER

Compiled by The Puzzle House

Answers to all puzzles can be found at the back of this book, starting on page 43.

Henderson Publishing
Woodbridge, England

1 BODY BUILDERS

Complete the words below by filling in the blanks with the name of part of the body. The first one is done to start you off.

1 F _L_ _I_ _P_ P E R

2 A P P _ _ _

3 C _ _ _ _ _

4 C H _ _ _ I N G

5 T E A _ _ _ _ G

6 _ _ _ _ SOME

2 FRIENDLY FACE

Use the letters in the face to work out the person's name.

3 CONFUSEDAY

If it's March and yesterday's tomorrow was Tuesday, what day will it be on the day after tomorrow's yesterday? (Actually, March has nothing to do with it . . . that's just to put you off!).

4 MAGIC

A magician had seven daughters and they each had a brother. How many children did the magician have?

5 MYSTERY GIRL

Can you find a girl's name that has SEVEN letters in it, yet contains only THREE different letters?

6 BRICK-A-BACK

Put the bricks back in the wall to reveal the message written there. The first letter of the notice is P.

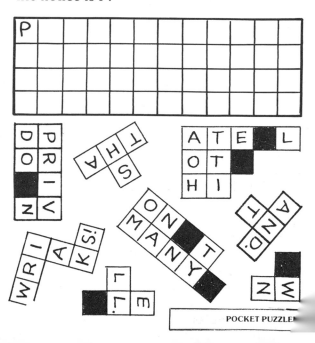

7 ALL CHANGE

How do you turn something into a clock?
Easy, you start with the word THING, then
change a letter at a time making a new
word with each move until you strike the
CLOCK. Use the clues to help you find the
in-between words.

T H I N G

_ _ _ _ _   **Concentrate your mind**

_ _ _ _ _   **Unkind description for
someone not too bright**

_ _ _ _ _   **Young bird**

_ _ _ _ _   **Noise of a camera
shutter**

C L O C K

8 THE BIG MATCH

Make the pattern shown here. Now remove
TWO matches (no more and no less) so
that the pattern is now made up of just two
squares.

NEVER EVER USE LIVE
MATCHES!
MAKE SURE THE MATCHES
HAVE BEEN USED OR ELSE
TRY THE PUZZLE WITH
STRAWS, PENS OR
PENCILS THAT ARE THE
SAME SIZE.

9 WHO AM I?

My first is in tartan,
But isn't in check.
My second is in collar,
But isn't in neck.
My third is in after,
But not in before.
My fourth is in window,
But isn't in door.
My last is in plant,
But isn't in tree.
Have you discovered
What I could be?

10 BREAKERS

Each group of ten letters can be broken
down into TWO words of five letters. Words
read from left to right and the letters are in
the correct order.

1 HOZRESBERA

 _ _ _ _ _ / _ _ _ _ _
 Clue: Two animals

2 PAPEPALCEH

 _ _ _ _ _ / _ _ _ _ _
 Clue: Two fruits

3 DSRCEASRSF

 _ _ _ _ _ / _ _ _ _ _
 Clue: Two things to wear

11 OK?

It's a simple sum, but we've put letters of the alphabet in place of numbers. Can you work out which two numbers are represented by the letters O and K in this addition sum?

```
   K
   K
  K+
 ____
  OK
```

12 SHOE'S WHO?

Which of the shoes shown below made the footprint shown here?

1.

2.

3.

4.

5.

6.

7.

13 NUMBER SQUARE

Using the numbers 1,2,3,4,5,6,7,8 and 9 fill the square so that each row reading across, each column reading down, and the two diagonals all add up to give the same total. Four numbers are in place for you.

14 GIRL SEARCH

Search out the girl's names from the sentences. Find the names by joining together words or parts of words, as shown in the first example.

1   is the <u>car ol</u>d?

   ANSWER: _____

2   Tell them many happy returns.

   ANSWER: _____

3   The tide will continue to rise and ebb I expect.

   ANSWER: _____

4   In the garden I see many flowers.

   ANSWER: _____

15 CARTOON CAPERS

TV cartoon and puppet characters have been boxed in the letter grid. See if you can search them all out. Words appear as a straight line and can read up, down, across, back or diagonally.

BAMBI	FLINTSTONES	POPEYE
BANANAMAN	JERRY	SCOOBY DOO
BATMAN	MICKEY	SNORKS
BUGS BUNNY	MUPPETS	SPOT
DONALD	OVIDE	TOM
DROIDS	PINK PANTHER	TOP CAT
DUMBO	PLUTO	YOGI

P	C	T	O	P	C	A	T	M	I
I	O	S	F	O	V	I	D	E	K
N	B	N	L	J	I	B	M	A	B
K	M	O	I	Y	E	Y	O	G	I
P	U	R	N	E	U	R	O	E	Y
A	D	K	T	K	S	S	R	M	B
N	L	S	S	C	D	T	E	Y	A
T	A	L	T	I	O	P	N	B	N
H	N	U	O	M	O	N	P	A	A
E	O	R	N	P	U	L	N	T	N
R	D	T	E	B	U	A	O	M	A
O	F	Y	S	T	E	P	P	U	M
L	E	G	O	S	S	A	N	P	A
I	U	N	T	B	A	T	M	A	N
B	S	C	O	O	B	Y	D	O	O

16 BLOCKHEADS

A word square reads the same whether you look at it across or down. Here's an example:

```
S T O P
T A M E
O M E N
P E N S
```

Use the listed words to form two word squares. There's a letter start.

AREA
CHEW
DART
EDGE

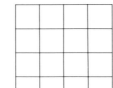

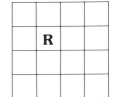

R

HIDE   REAL   TALL   WEEK

17 A FRIENDLY FACE

Use the letters in the face to work out the person's name.

18 HOW COME?

Two fathers and two sons went to a football match. Each bought a match-day programme, yet between them they only had three programmes How come?

19 WHAT'S NEXT?

Fill in the blanks with the two numbers or letters which are next in the series.

1. 1 3 5 7 9 ___ ___

2. 2 4 7 11 16 ___ ___

3. Z Y X W V ___ ___

4. A E I M Q ___ ___

5. 2 4 8 16 32 ___ ___

20 COLOUR MATCH

Match the colours to complete the song titles.

BROWN GOLD RED WHITE YELLOW

LADY IN _____

_____ SUBMARINE

_____ CHRISTMAS

_____ FINGER

_____ SUGAR

21 OCTO-PUZZLE

Take EIGHT EIGHTS ... that's 8 and 8 and 8 and 8 and 8 and 8 and 8 and 8 ... and form an addition sum that totals 1,000

22 FOREWORD

What word can go in front of all these words?

SHELF   MARK   TOKEN

23 TRIANGULAR

How many triangles are there in the drawing?

24 WHAT'S COOKING?

Hidden in the sentences is a cooking term which involves raising the temperature. Find the words by joining together words or parts of words.

1   She attends the school down the road.

    ANSWER: _____

2   It was a drab oil painting of little value.

    ANSWER: _____

3   After war most of us wish for peace.

    ANSWER: _____

25 EYE-SPY

Use your eyes to find five items that a master spy would try to smuggle out of a country. Start at the letter top left and move from letter to letter in any direction except diagonally to spell out the items.

```
M R O F I L
I C A L P M
S S N L E S
E E T I F E
C R S C O D
```

26 SIX OF THE BEST

What number gives the same result whether you multiply it by 6 or add 6 to it?

27 THE BIG MATCH

Form the pattern below with matches. REMEMBER NEVER USE LIVE MATCHES! Now move just THREE matches so that you make a figure containing FOUR squares.

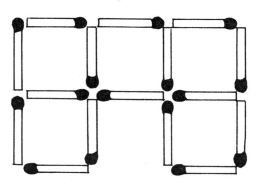

28 FOLLOW MY LEADER

Which word can follow ALL of these words?

ALARM   CARRIAGE

GRANDFATHER   GRANDMOTHER

29 HOW CAN?

How can you turn a CARTHORSE into a group of musicians?

30 CODEBUSTER

Crack the code and discover the codebuster message. The password is BANANA, which is written in code as CBOBOB. Using that information what does the message below say?

T F D S F U   B H F O U

D I B S M J F   B S S J W F T

B U   N J E O J H I U

31 SOUNDPROOF

Certain pairs SOUND the same although they are spelt differently, like HIM and HYMN. Try to work out a pair of similar sounding words for each clue.

1 Midriff rubbish

ANSWER:_____ / _____

2 Type of herb measured by a clock

ANSWER:_____ / _____

3 Trapped on a tennis pitch

ANSWER:_____ / _____

4 Put pen to paper, that's correct

ANSWER:_____ / _____

32 FIT-BACK

Fit the words back into the frame. Words can read either across or down. There's only one possible solution.

2 Letters

ME   NO

5 Letters

AGENT   CAMEL

3 Letters

COG   DOT   EAT
HOT   SIR   SKI

6 Letters

OYSTER   RIGHTS

7 Letters

AIRPORT

INVADED

BANDAGE

WEDDING

8 Letters

ACCIDENT

THIRTEEN

33 SPOT THE DIFFERENCE

There are SIX differences between the two pictures. Can you spot the lot?

34 WHAT AM I?

My first is in conker,
But isn't in tree.
My second's in too,
But isn't in tea.
My third is in cow,
But isn't in ox.
My fourth is in shoe,
And also in socks.
My fifth is in thank,
But isn't in think,
Have you discovered
A hot bedtime drink?

35 FRIENDLY FACE

Use the letters in the face to work out the person's name.

36 FOLLOW MY LEADER

Which word can follow ALL of these words?

ARM   DINING   HIGH   ROCKING

37 BATTY!

Batboy, the internationally known crime-fighter, has been trapped by his fiendish foe, The Jester! Our hero regains consciousness to discover that he is trapped in a rope web which is suspended over a lake of lumpy custard. Even as he looks round the underground cavern where he is imprisoned, an army of The Jester's giant moths come out of the gloom, flapping remorselessly towards him . . .! Time for action! Batboy has one match left in his Bat-belt. Two brilliant escape plans crash creatively into the caped crusader's cranium. He can either use the match to burn strands of rope, fall into the custard lake with such force that lumps of custard will be propelled like missiles to bombard the flying moths . . . OR, he reckons he can just reach some paper left close by in a crevice in the rock wall, and start a fire — knowing that the light will distract the moths.

The moths get closer . . . the custard looks lumpier . . . Batboy looks at the rope, the paper and his one remaining match. What should he light first?

38 NUGS TO YOU!

Can you make FOUR different words using the letters
N U G S ?

39 RIGHT ON Q

See if you can search out all the listed words beginning with the letter Q. Words appear in straight lines that can read across, back, up, down or diagonally.

QUACK	QUARREL	QUERY	QUINCE
QUAD	QUARRY	QUESTION	QUIP
QUAIL	QUARTET	QUEUE	QUIT
QUAINT	QUARTZ	QUICK	QUIVER
QUAKE	QUASH	QUID	QUIZ
QUAKER	QUEEN	QUIET	QUOTE
QUALITY	QUEER	QUILL	
QUARANTINE	QUENCH	QUILT	

Q	U	I	T	Q	U	I	V	E	R
U	U	K	C	A	U	Q	U	N	Y
E	Q	I	R	E	E	U	Q	I	T
S	U	Q	N	Q	U	I	U	T	I
T	Q	U	I	C	K	L	E	N	L
I	Q	U	A	K	E	L	N	A	A
O	D	R	E	Y	E	I	C	R	U
N	A	E	U	R	U	A	H	A	Q
E	U	K	R	R	Y	U	Q	U	U
E	Q	A	U	A	Q	Q	Q	Q	A
U	U	U	Q	U	Q	U	U	Q	R
Q	E	Q	O	Q	U	A	I	N	T
U	U	T	U	Q	R	U	D	L	E
I	E	I	Q	T	Q	U	I	E	T
P	Q	U	Z	Q	U	A	Y	U	Q

40 CODED COUNTRIES

All the words below can have their letters moved around to form the name of a country. The first one is done for you.

1 R A I N   I R A N

2 P A I N S   _____

3 P U R E   _____

4 C H A I N   _____

5 S E R I A L   *ISREAL*

6 R U M B A   _____

7 I N L A C E D   *ICELAND*

8 E N G L A N D E R   _____

41 NUMBER NAMES

A D E J N Y

Each of these letters has been given a numerical value from 1 to 6. No two different letters have the same value.

Adding up the values together

DAN is worth 6.

JAN is worth 11

EDNA is worth 11

What will ANDY be worth?

1 2 3 4 5 6
D A N Y E J

42 TIME'S UP

What time of day appears the same whether it is spelt backwards or forwards or looked at upside down?

43 SHADY

Which of the silhouettes is the exact match of the figure shown here?

44 ODDS 'N' EVENS

The word JAUNTY can be split up into two
shorter words — JUT and ANY — by
separating the odd and even numbers. So
take letters 1, 3, 5 for one word and 2, 4, 6
for another.
The eight words below were formed in the
same way. Your problem is to try and pair
them back together and make FOUR
words of six letters.

ASS   FUN   LET   SIT

SOG   SUD   TOE   TRY

45 MATCH OF THE DAY

Start off with this pattern made from
USED matches. Now move TWO matches
and make a pattern of SEVEN squares.

46 FOREWORD

Which word can go in front of all these
words?

BIRD   BOARD   BERRY

47 SING-A-LONG

A man was looking at a photograph when he suddenly burst into song. (You can join him if you like . . . try the tune of 'The Locomotion' or 'Baa-Baa Black Sheep', or both!)

"Brothers and sisters

I have none,

Yet this man's father

Is my father's son."

Who was the man looking at?

48 ALL CHANGE

All change to get from DOVER in Kent, England to RIPON in Yorkshire, England. Change one letter at a time and make a new word with each move, using the clues to help you.

D O V E R

_ _ _ _ _   Person who explores underwater

_ _ _ _ _   Flows through the land

_ _ _ _ _   More ready to eat of the two

_ _ _ _ _   Become ready to be picked

R I P O N

49 BE A SPORT

The name of a sport or game is hidden in each of the sentences below. Be a sport and try to sort them out. You'll find that by joining words — or parts of words — together you can find the answers.

1   Put the rug by the bed

   ANSWER: _____

2   The churches sometimes are in need of repair

   ANSWER: _____

3   Grandad's taking his nap at the moment

   ANSWER: _____

4   Bella crossed the road at the crossing

   ANSWER: _____

5   Among the tasty sweets there was a bad mint on that plate

   ANSWER: _____

50 EGGSPERT

In a very large pan full of water it takes 3 and a half minutes to boil TWO eggs. How long will it take to boil FOUR eggs in the same pan?

51 JUST TESTING

What was the largest island in the Southern hemisphere before Australia was discovered!

52 MEMORY TEST

Take a careful look at this picture. You have exactly one minute to look at it. Then, turn the page and see if you can answer the memory questions.

1 Was the bedroom door open or closed?
2 And what about the window . . . open or closed?
3 Was there a wall light switch or a cord switch?
4 There was a cup on the bedside table. How many handles did it have?
5 What animal was shown on the wall poster?
6 Was there a model plane in the room?
7 Curtains had stripes on them. Were the black stripes thicker than the white ones . . . or was it the other way round?
8 What times was it according to the wall clock?

53 FRUIT & GEV

Yes, it should have been VEG, but that's just to give you the idea of this puzzle. All the words below can have their letters moved around to give the name of a fruit or vegetable.

1 R E A P   PEAR

2 C H E A P   _____

3 L U M P   _____

4 A P E   _____

5 M I L E   _____

54 WHOLE WORDS

Fill the holes in the words by using another word. Use the same word for the three examples in each group. We've done the first one for you.

1   M I T T E N
    T E N T
    A T T E N D

2   _ _ _ R
    S _ _ _ M
    _ _ _ C H E R

3   _ _ _ T A I N
    E S _ _ _ E
    _ _ _ E

4   _ _ _ T E R
    V I O _ _ _
    B A L _ _ _

5   V A C _ _ _
    _ _ _ L E R
    C _ _ _ E E N

55 WHAT'S NEXT?

Fill in the blanks with the two things which are next in the series.

1. **December October August**

   _____ _____

2. **Mon Thurs Sun**

   _____ _____

3. **2.30 3.35 4.40** _____ _____

4. **O T T F F S S E** _____ _____

56 IN THE CAN

The words described below all start with the same three letters ... C A N. Can you work out all the answers?

1 **Call off, as with a sports fixture**

   C A N _ _ _

2 **Sweet, especially in America**

   C A N _ _

3 **Wax light**

   C A N _ _ _

4 **Tent may be made of this**

   C A N _ _ _

5 **Person who eats flesh of others**

   C A N _ _ _ _ _

57 UNCLE MONEYBAGS

Uncle Moneybags decided to divide £1,000 between his three nephews — Alan, Bill and Colin — and their wives. Alan got £20 more than Bill, and £40 more than Colin. Each of the wives got more than their husbands did. Alan's wife got twice the amount given to Alan. The same happened to Colin and his wife. And Bill's wife got three times the amount that Bill did. How much did each couple receive from Uncle Moneybags?

58 ALL SQUARE

A word square reads the same across and down. The DRUM is your starter but you still need three more words to finish the word square. The words can be found hidden in the letter square, reading in straight lines going in any direction.

D	R	U	M
R			
U			
M			

E	T	E	E	M
E	G	R	U	D
T	A	R	G	M
R	E	M	D	U
M	T	R	U	G

Each letter which slots into the frame has a number. We have given you two words with their number codes to start you off. Keep a record of which number represents which letter in the smaller grid, and find the words to fit the frame.

7	3	8	4	5	9	■	7 S	■	7	■
5	■	3	■	1	14	5 T	17	13	16	
1 E	2 X	3 P	1 E	4 R	5 T	■	14 A	■	1	■
4	■	8	14	■	18	17 I	20	1	8	
1	■	7	8	6	5	1	4 R	■	19	■
8	11	1	■	6	■	13	■	10	1	5
■	8	■	3	15	1	20	16	1	■	4
25	26	1	26	1	■	8	■	4	■	1
■	13	■	3	■	24	4	8	23	1	13
14	20	12	17	4	1	■	■	17	■	21
■	7	■	15	■	20	4	1	13	21	22

1 E	2 X	3 P	4 R	5 T	6	7 S	8	9	10	11	12	13
14 A	15	16	17 I	18	19	20	21	22	23	24	25	26

60 MAZE

Which path leads to the hidden treasure?

61 REFILL

Complete the words below by filling in the blanks with the name of an animal. The first is done to start you off.

1   B <u>O</u> <u>X</u> E S

2   S _ _ _ T E R

3   _ _ _ T L E

4   D A N D E _ _ _ _ _

5   S _ _ _ _ _

62 DUCK TALE

Ducks swimming on a pond. Two ducks in front of a duck, two ducks behind a duck, and one duck in the middle. How many ducks altogether?

63 FRUIT SALAD

Start at the letter top left and move one letter at a time. You can move in any direction except on a diagonal, to spell out the names of five different fruits.

A P P L I
P E L A M
E N A N E
A A B E G
R O R A N

64 BOY SEARCH

Search out the boy's name in each sentence. Find the names by joining together words or parts of words as in the first example.

1 They recorded the disc live at Wembley

ANSWER: _____

2 On the cliff ran Kate and her friends

ANSWER: _____

3 I'm usually in a jam especially at school

ANSWER: _____

4 Which part hurts most?

ANSWER: _____

5 We tidy the stage or generally help the actors

ANSWER: _____

65 FOLLOW MY LEADER

Which word can follow ALL these words?

BAG   DRAIN   HORN   WIND

66 MACHINE HUNT

Search out the names of machines hidden in the letter grid. Words appear in straight lines, up, down, across, back or diagonally.

CALCULATOR   PHONE
CAMERA   PLANE
CAR   PRINTER
COMPUTER   RADIO
COPIER   STEREO
DISHWASHER   TYPEWRITER
FAX   VIDEO
MICROWAVE

C	O	M	P	U	T	E	R	P	T
A	V	C	U	L	A	O	H	Y	R
L	C	I	X	S	T	O	P	A	C
C	R	A	D	T	N	E	D	C	A
U	F	C	R	E	W	I	A	L	M
L	M	I	C	R	O	W	A	V	E
A	O	M	I	E	N	A	L	P	R
T	P	T	C	O	P	I	E	R	A
O	E	U	R	E	T	N	I	R	P
R	E	H	S	A	W	H	S	I	D

67 FAMILY PROBLEM

A doctor in Birmingham had a brother in Newcastle who was a solicitor. But the solicitor in Newcastle did not have a brother in Birmingham who was a doctor. Why not?

68 TEASING TRIANGLES

How many triangles can you count in the figure?

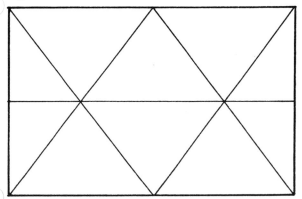

69 FARMER BROWN'S ORCHARD

Farmer Brown had an orchard of fruit trees. A third of them were apple trees, a quarter were pear trees, and a fifth were plum trees. There were twenty-six cherry trees. How many trees did Farmer Brown have altogether?

70 BREAKERS

Each group of ten letters can be broken
down into TWO words of five letters. Words
read from left to right and the letters are in
the correct order. Can you make the
break? There's a clue in each case.

1   J A C P H I N A N A

     _ _ _ _ _ / _ _ _ _ _

     Clue: Two countries

2   H I O G L U O S O E

     _ _ _ _ _ / _ _ _ _ _

     Clue: Two places to live

3   E A R G O B L I N E

     _ _ _ _ _ / _ _ _ _ _

     Clue: Two birds

4   M O T E U T H E T H

     _ _ _ _ _ / _ _ _ _ _

     Clue: Two parts of the face

5   M A R A P C R I H L

     _ _ _ _ _ / _ _ _ _ _

     Clue: Two months

71 PIG POSER

Why is the letter K like the tail of a pig?

72 A FRIENDLY FACE

Use the letters in the face to work out the person's name.

73 STORYGRAM

Complete the story by filling in the missing words. Each word is made up using only the letters from the word in capital letters.

When we go to the park we take STALE

bread to feed to the ducks. Gran tells us

__ __ __ __ __ of when she was little.

Now she must be at __ __ __ __ __ a

hundred. She lives in a cottage with a

__ __ __ __ __ roof. She chases away

rabbits who try to __ __ __ __ __ lettuces

from her garden.

74 LINKS

What's the link between RICE, STEAMED, QUEEN and YORKSHIRE?

75 ALL CHANGE

Changing a letter at a time and making a new word with each move change the word STORK to the word CHASE. Use the clues to help you find the in between words. Good hunting!

S T O R K

_ _ _ _ _   **Place where things are kept for some time**

_ _ _ _ _   **Land by the sea**

_ _ _ _ _   **Dull, boring job**

_ _ _ _ _   **Picked**

C H A S E

76 NUMBER SQUARE

Using the numbers 2, 3, 4, 4, 5, 6, 6, 7, 8 fill the squares so that each row reading across, each row reading down and the two diagonals add up to the same total. 3 numbers are in place for you.

4		
	5	
		6

77 FITBACK

Fit the words back into the frame. Words can read either across or down. There's only one possible solution.

2 Letters

AN   MA   ON   SO

3 Letters

OWN   RUN

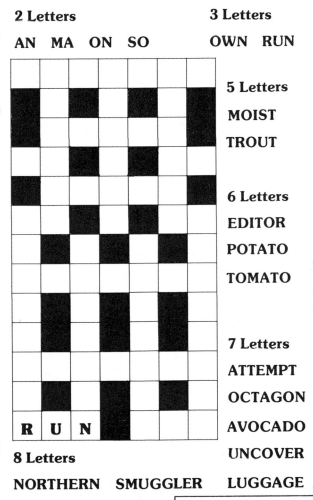

5 Letters

MOIST

TROUT

6 Letters

EDITOR

POTATO

TOMATO

7 Letters

ATTEMPT

OCTAGON

AVOCADO

UNCOVER

8 Letters

NORTHERN   SMUGGLER

LUGGAGE

78 MONKEYING AROUND

Which of the five monkeys in the picture is the odd one out?

79 WHAT AM I?

My first is in apricot but isn't in peach
My second's in sand but isn't in beach
My third is in high but isn't in bough
My fourth's not in why, but it is there in how
My last is in lunch, are you anywhere near?
Sometimes when you meet me you may shed a tear.

80 SOCK PROBLEM

There are 12 socks in a drawer, six green and six brown. There's been a power cut so the room is dark. How many socks would you need to take out of the drawer to be sure you had a pair of socks, either two green or two brown?

81 FORWORD

Which word can go in front of all these words?

CHOCOLATE   FLOAT   MAN

82 NUMBER'S UP

If you add 1,480 to a certain number, the result will be more than if you multiplied that number by 1,480. What is the number?

83 FISHY BUSINESS

In the list below the letters needed to complete the words are the names of fish. Can you sort out this fishy business and complete the words?

1   E M _ _ _ _ Y

2   _ _ _ _ B Y

3   _ _ _ B L E

4   S _ _ _ _ S P E A R E

5   D E _ _ _ E

6   F _ _ _ I N G

7   S _ _ _ _ D

8   I N _ _ _ _ N T

9   A P P _ _ _ _ _

10 S _ _ _ _ O W

84 NAMEGRAMS

The names of TEN boys and girls have been mixed up and made into other words. Rearrange the letters in each word, and give the boys and girls their names back.

RADIAN   DENIAL   WANDER

EVENTS   INGLE   ALIENS   DANGLE

ORACLE   TAKE   HURT

ANSWERS

1. Body Builders
1 Lip. 2 Ear. 3 Hair. 4 Arm. 5 Chin. 6 Hand.

2. Friendly Face
Trevor

3. Confuseday
Wednesday

4. Magic
Eight. Seven daughters and one son.

5. Mystery Girl
Barbara

6. Brick-A-Back

P	R	I	V	A	T	E		L	A	N	D
D	O		N	O	T		W	R	I	T	E
O	N		T	H	I	S		W	A	L	L
M	A	N	Y		T	H	A	N	K	S!	

7. All Change
Thing-Think-Thick-Chick-Click-Clock

8. The Big Match

9. Who Am I?
Train

10. Breakers
1 Horse/Zebra.
2 Peach/Apple.
3 Dress/Scarf.

11. OK?
$0 = 1$ $K = 5$ So $5 + 5 + 5 = 15$

12. Shoe's Who
5

13. Number Square
6 1 8
7 5 3
2 9 4

14. Girl Search
1 Carol. 2 Emma.
3 Debbie. 4 Denise.

15. Cartoon Capers

16. Blockheads

```
C H E W     D A R T
H I D E     A R E A
E D G E     R E A L
W E E K     T A L L
```

17. A Friendly Face
Thomas

18. How Come?
A grandfather, his son and grandson. Three people but two fathers and two sons.

19. What's Next?
1.11 13 Adding 2 each time. 2. 22 29 Adding a number increasing by 1 each time. 3. U T Working back through the alphabet. 4. U Y Miss out three letters at a time going through the alphabet. 5. 64 128 Double the previous number.

20. Colour Match
Lady In Red · Yellow Submarine · White Christmas · Gold Finger · Brown Sugar.

21. Octo-Puzzle
$888 + 88 + 8 + 8 + 8 = 1,000$

22. Foreword
Book

23. Triangular
22

24. What's Cooking?
1 Heat. 2 Boil. 3 Warm.

25. Eye-Spy
Microfilm · Plans · Secrets · Code · Files

26. Six Of The Best
1.2

27. The Big Match

28. Follow My Leader
Clock

29. How Can?
Rearrange the letters so CARTHORSE becomes ORCHESTRA

30. Codebuster
All letters move forward one place in the alphabet. A becomes B, B becomes C etc.
Message reads : SECRET AGENT CHARLIE ARRIVES AT MIDNIGHT

31. Soundproof
1 Waist/Waste.
2 Thyme/Time.
3 Caught/Court.
4 Write/Right.

32. Fit-Back

33. Spot The Difference

36. Follow My Leader
Chair

38. Nugs to You!
Gnus · Guns · Snug · Sung.

40. Coded Countries
1 Iran. 2 Spain. 3 Peru.
4 China. 5 Israel. 6 Burma.
7 Iceland. 8 Greenland.

41. Number Names
Andy is worth 10. A = 2 or 3,
D = 1, E = 5, J = 6,
N = 2 or 3, Y = 4

42. Time's Up
Noon

43. Shady
E

34. What Am I?
Cocoa

35. Friendly Face
Denise

37. Batty
He lit the match first.

39. Right On Q

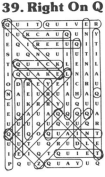

44. Odds 'N' Evens
Assist · Fluent · Stooge · Sturdy

45. Match Of The Day

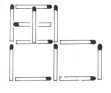

46. Foreword
Black

47. Sing-A-Long
The man is looking at a
photo of his own son.

48. All Change
Dover · Diver · River · Riper · Ripen · Ripon.

49. Be A Sport
1 Rugby. 2 Chess. 3 Snap. 4 Lacrosse.
5 Badminton.

50. Eggspert
3½ minutes. It was a large pan so there will be
enough room for all the eggs to boil together.

51. Just Testing
Australia . . . it was still there! Didn't fall for it
did you?

52. Memory Test
You can now turn back and check for yourself.

53. Fruit & Gev
1 Pear. 2 Peach. 3 Plum. 4 Pea. 5 Lime.

54. Whole Words
1 TEN · Mitten, Tent, Attend. 2 TEA · Tear,
Steam, Teacher. 3 CAP · Captain, Escape, Cape.
4 LET · Letter, Violet, Ballet. 5 ANT · Vacant,
Antler, Canteen.

55. What's Next?
1 June/April. 2 Wednesday/Saturday. 3 5.45/6.50.
4 N/T (One, Two, Three, Four etc).

56. In The Can
1 Cancel. 2 Candy. 3 Candle. 4 Canvas. 5 Cannibal.

57. Uncle Moneybags
Alan gets £120, his wife £240.
Combined they get £360.
Bill gets £100, his wife £300.
Combined they get £400.
Colin gets £80, his wife £160.
Combined they get £240.

58. All Square
```
D R U M
R A R E
U R G E
M E E T
```

59. Codenumber

60. Maze

61. Refill
1 Ox. 2 Cat. 3 Rat.
4 Lion. 5 Hare.
62. Duck Tale
3
63. Fruit Salad
Apple · Pear · Orange
Banana · Lime.
64. Boy Search
1 Clive. 2 Frank.
3 James. 4 Arthur.
5 George.

66. Machine Hunt

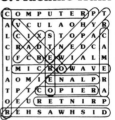

65. Follow My Leader
Pipe
67. Family Problem
The doctor in Birmingham
was the sister of the
solicitor in Newcastle.
68. Teasing Triangles
18
69. Farmer Brown's Orchard
120
70. Breakers
1 Japan/China. 2 House/Igloo. 3 Eagle/Robin.
4 Mouth/Teeth. 5 March/April.
71. Pig Poser
Because they are both at the end of a
SQUEAK.
72. A Friendly Face
Charles
73. Storygram
Tales · Least · Slate · Steal
74. Links
They are all types of pudding.
75. All Change
Stork · Store · Shore · Chore · Chose ·
Chase.

76. Number Square

```
4  8  3
4  5  6
7  2  6
```

77. Fitback

A	T	T	E	M	P	T
	O		D		O	
	M	O	I	S	T	
M	A		T		A	N
	T	R	O	U	T	
S	O		R		O	N
M		O		A		O
U	N	C	O	V	E	R
G		T		O		T
G		A		C		H
L	U	G	G	A	G	E
E		O		D		R
R	U	N		O	W	N

78. Monkeying Around
Odd one out is C.

79. What Am I?
Onion.

80. Sock Problem
3. If the first is brown and the second is green then the third must make a pair.

81. Foreword
Milk.

82. Number's Up
The number 1.

83. Fishy Business
1 Bass · 2 Chub · 3 Dab · 4 Hake · 5 Cod ·
6 Eel · 7 Pike · 8 Sole · 9 Roach · 10 Parr.

84. Namegrams
Adrian · Daniel · Andrew · Steven · Nigel ·
Selina · Glenda · Carole · Kate · Ruth.

I GIVE UP!!